Jon was introduced to the puppies – and there were lots of them: little Labrador retrievers, all tiny and squashed up, with wrinkly faces, nudging and shoving each other out of the way, yapping and blinking their little eyes. Jon stood over them, grinning as they played about, slowly getting used to their little stubby legs. And then one of them caught his attention.

She was a little girl, jet-black and pudgy – and very cute! As Jon watched, she marched right through the middle of a tub of mushed-up dog food, gulping down bits of it as she went. Mid-mouthful, she looked up and caught Jon staring at her. Immediately her alert eyes focused on him. *Who are you?* she seemed to be asking.

Also available by Jon Katz for younger readers:

The Totally True Story of Devon,
The Naughtiest Dog in the World

Rose and Izzy the Cheekiest Dogs on the Farm

Available for adult readers and
published by Random House:

A Dog Year: Rescuing Devon,
the most troublesome dog in the world

A Home for Rose: How my life
turned upside down for the love of a dog

A Good Dog: The Story of Orson,
who changed my life

Saving Izzy: The abandoned dog
who stole my heart

The Dog Who Loved:
Lenore, the puppy who rescued me

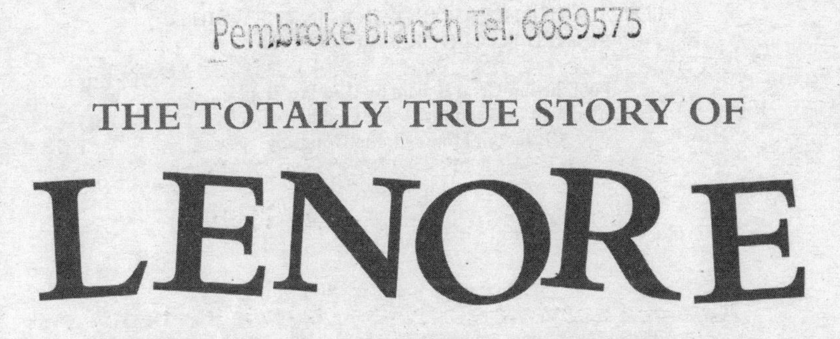

THE TOTALLY TRUE STORY OF

LENORE

The Hungriest Dog in the World

Based on the story by JON KATZ

Adapted for young readers by Ruth Knowles

LENORE: THE HUNGRIEST DOG IN THE WORLD
A RED FOX BOOK 978 1 849 41554 5

Published in Great Britain by Red Fox Books,
an imprint of Random House Children's Books
A Random House Group Company

This edition published 2011

1 3 5 7 9 10 8 6 4 2

Adapted for younger readers from *The Dog Who Loved; Lenore, the puppy who rescued me,* published in 2010 by Ebury Press, an imprint of Ebury Publishing, a Random House Group Company.
First published in the USA by Random House Inc, 2009

The Random House Group Limited supports The Forest Stewardship Council (FSC®), the leading international forest certification organisation. Our books carrying the FSC label are printed on FSC® certified paper. FSC is the only forest certification scheme endorsed by the leading environmental organisations, including Greenpeace.
Our paper procurement policy can be found at
www.randomhouse.co.uk/environment

Set in 14/20pt Bembo by Falcon Oast Graphic Art Ltd.

Red Fox Books are published by Random House Children's Books,
61–63 Uxbridge Road, London W5 5SA

www.**kidsatrandomhouse**.co.uk

Addresses for companies within The Random House Group Limited can be found at: www.randomhouse.co.uk/offices.htm

THE RANDOM HOUSE GROUP Limited Reg. No. 954009

A CIP catalogue record for this book is available from the British Library.

Printed and bound by CPI Group (UK) Ltd, Croydon, CR0 4YY

Thanks to Maria Wulf

LENORE

The Hungriest Dog in the World

CONTENTS

The Most Important Meal of the Day..........3
Swinging Around with Elvis......................13
Goating Around..21
Feeling Better..33
Saying Hello...43
A New Litter...55
Meet Lenore...61
Trouble at Bedtime.....................................69
Izzy Works His Magic...............................77
The Part-time Dog......................................87
It's Bedtime!...95
The Hungriest Dog in the World.............103
Into the Woods...113

CHAPTER ONE

The Most Important Meal of the Day

Early one morning Jon Katz headed out of his back door. He was hungry, but it wasn't time for *his* breakfast yet – he had lots of other mouths to feed first. Bedlam Farm, just outside New Jersey in the United States, now had more animals than it had ever had before: donkeys, sheep, chickens, cows, cats – and dogs, of course! They were Jon's favourite: not only was he a farmer, he also wrote lots of books about his dogs.

Once, he had just been a writer, but now his days were very different. Instead of the *tap-tap-tapitty-tap* of his keyboard, they were now full of braying, baaing, clucking, mooing, miaowing and barking – and the noise all started at breakfast time!

First Jon went over to his donkeys, Lulu, Fanny, Jeanette and Jesus. Their favourite breakfast was donkey cookies, and Jon knew that as soon as they heard him coming, they would rush over to the side of their pen to wait for him. It was a bright, cold day and the sun was shining in his eyes, but even as he squinted he could see that they were there, as usual!

As soon as he was close enough, the donkeys started braying loudly and excitedly, nudging his pockets with their soft brown noses to see what he had for them.

"Morning, guys!" Jon laughed. "Hang on,

hang on. It's coming!" And he managed to pull out the cookies for them.

They happily chewed away on their breakfast, raising their heads occasionally to stare at him with big thoughtful eyes.

Jon found the donkeys very peaceful animals and he loved spending time with them. But he couldn't just yet: he knew that the sound of the donkeys waking up for their breakfast would have the rest of Bedlam Farm anxiously waiting for theirs! So, with a goodbye pat on Lulu's head, Jon headed off to do the rest of his rounds.

All the animals on the farm loved food, but they were all totally different, with their own personalities – and so, of course, they had their own favourite thing to eat!

Meet the Animals of Bedlam Farm . . .

Winston the rooster and the chickens – favourite food is dry dog food

Lots of hens – they love bugs and chicken feed

The donkeys, Jeanette, Lulu, Fanny and Jesus – they like donkey cookies!

The barn cats, Mother and Minnie – enjoy mice, moles and cat food

Elvis the huge cow – he loves carrots and apples, but Dunkin' Donuts are his favourite!

Luna, Elvis's girlfriend – munches on lots of grass and hay

Lots of sheep (only two of my girl sheep have names – Paula, who was the first ewe I had (named after my wife), and Brutus, her son; the others all have numbers instead of name – Number 57 is one of my favourites) – they like eating hay

The dogs – love their liver treats

Once outdoor breakfast duties were over, Jon headed back inside. As soon as he did so, his two black-and-white Border collies, Rose and Izzy, were at his heels in a flash. Jon always felt better when they were around, and he bent to stroke each of them in turn. "Morning, Rose. How are you today?" he asked. And, "Another busy day for us today, Izzy. Are you up for it, fellow?"

They were both clever little dogs and they spent a lot of time with each other, and with Jon. They looked up at him as if in answer to his questions: *I'm good – ready to get started herding those sheep*, Rose seemed to be saying. And, *I love busy days – I'll be wherever you are!* from Izzy.

Jon's dogs were a huge part of his life. This morning was totally normal: wherever he went – on the farm or in his house, to a book signing, or out for dinner – one of his dogs was there with him.

He walked over to the kitchen table to

cut a slice of bread. Sensing a shadow at his side, he held out the slice. Izzy was there, having followed him, padding along almost silently, and he immediately gulped down the bread before rubbing up against Jon's legs and wagging his tail happily to say thank you. Izzy seemed totally settled and happy now, but as Jon cut himself another slice of bread, he thought back to when he'd first met Izzy. Things were very different then . . .

Jon had been hearing about Izzy for months before he finally met him. The little dog had been abandoned by his owners, left alone to run up and down along a fence, half-mad. It was very, very sad – whenever he heard about Izzy, tears would come into Jon's eyes.

One of the first books Jon had written had been about his old dog, Devon, who had also been abandoned – until Jon took him in and trained him and loved him. Since then, lots of people had called him up whenever they heard about a dog in need, to see if he could help. But he had to be careful. He had a farm to look after, and three dogs: Rose and Clementine and Pearl (Devon had very sadly died by then). Helping dogs in need took a lot of time and care and energy. It was very worthwhile, but Jon didn't think he was strong enough, or had enough time, to do it over and over again.

But with Izzy, Jon hadn't been able to resist. Once his friend Flo had talked him into going to see Izzy, he knew she was right: Izzy was worth saving. And Jon couldn't leave him there alone. His owners had bought him to herd sheep, but they had never got the sheep, and they'd left the farm completely – abandoning Izzy too.

Jon knew that sometimes a dog and a human find one another and fit together perfectly, loving each other totally. Izzy and Jon had hit the jackpot. There had been some tough times, but as soon as Izzy decided to become Jon's dog, things had been great. He and Jon were pals and companions, and that was that.

IZZY THEN

Izzy was very upset when Jon had first met him, with wide, wild brown eyes, saliva dripping from his mouth, his head constantly jerking about. He was on the move all the time – like a one-dog merry-go-round! He was filthy, his black and white coat caked in mud – and very smelly!

But even through all this, Jon could see that Izzy was still beautiful: his body was long and graceful, and sometimes he would hold his head up proudly and look at Jon as if to say, *I'm better than this.*

Things were tough back then. Izzy couldn't travel in cars: they scared him so much that he was sick, and he would poo all over the seats every time he got in. And it wasn't just the car he was frightened of: he was scared in the house, which meant he destroyed things there whenever he got the chance. He was scared in his sleeping crate, so he messed that up too, flinging himself at the kitchen door again and again, trying to escape. And he was scared on the farm too, so he would constantly try and run away by jumping over the fences as if he were a racehorse.

IZZY NOW

Things now were very different. The wild Izzy from the farm was long gone, and every time Jon looked at his little Border collie, his heart filled with pride.

Izzy was a real charmer! Whenever he met somebody new, he would flash his big brown eyes at them before padding over for a hug, or to rest his head on their knee. He generally preferred women to men – *What a flirt!* Jon always thought.

He also totally trusted Jon and went everywhere with him – without ever being put on a lead. When his master was working, the little dog would sit under his desk; when he went out, Izzy would hop easily into the car and rest his head near Jon's hand while he was driving. He even slept under Jon's bed some nights!

Occasionally Jon would look down at Izzy and notice that the little Border collie was gazing up at him thoughtfully with sad eyes, sometimes even letting out a long doggy sigh. When this happened, Jon wondered whether Izzy was thinking back a few years to that horrible time when all he could do was run up and down, up and down, with no company and, most importantly, no love.

CHAPTER TWO

Swinging Around with Elvis

Izzy had now been on the farm with Jon for a few years, and though he loved Jon – and people in general – very much, he wasn't that bothered about other animals. Except for Rose, that is. He loved Rose more than anything. He quite liked the donkeys – especially Lulu: he would sit in front of her for hours, letting her sniff at him with her long soft shaggy nose – but it was definitely Rose who had his heart.

And Rose had Jon's heart too; he didn't know what he would do without her. She was a black and white Border collie, like Izzy, and was now six years old. She had bright, intelligent dark eyes and she seemed to know what Jon wanted even before he spoke to her. She had the sheep wrapped around her little finger and was the best herder Jon – and his farmer friends – had ever seen! She was Jon's right-hand girl.

As well as Rose and Izzy, Jon had two other dogs: Pearl and Clementine, both big, friendly golden Labradors. But neither of them were on the farm any more. Pearl now lived with Jon's daughter, Emma, in Brooklyn. She and Pearl had always got on well, and Emma missed her terribly when she was away in the city. Clementine had also gone to live with somebody else – Jon's friend, Ali. Clementine was very energetic and needed lots of time and energy devoted to her; with two other dogs and all the other animals on the farm, Jon had felt unable to give her all the attention that he knew was important to her, so when Ali had said that she was looking for a dog, Jon offered to lend her Clementine to see how they got on together. They soon became the best of friends, and so Clem now spent most of her time with Ali.

Jon missed his Labradors, but he still got to see them – and he and Rose and Izzy got on brilliantly. They were a team, and he knew that no matter what mood he was in, they would cheer him up. As long as he kept up his side of the bargain – to feed, exercise and love them – Rose and Izzy would love him back, and that was a wonderful feeling.

Although Rose and Izzy had made him smile that morning, Jon was feeling tired. He was beginning to find the farm work – on top of all his writing – very hard, and he felt like he needed to relax a little more. Paula, Jon's wife, didn't live on the farm the whole time as she taught at a school in New York. She was teaching at the moment, and so Jon decided to pay Elvis a visit.

Apart from the dogs, Jon's other favourite animal was Elvis, the huge cow. Bulls like Elvis can be very dangerous creatures, and Jon would never go up to one he didn't know, but Elvis was the most contented creature Jon had ever met, and whenever he felt low or down in the dumps, Elvis was there, waiting to listen to him. The cow had always reminded Jon a little of Shrek – he was so big and scary-looking, but once you got to know him, he was as soft and gentle as a big teddy bear. But he certainly wasn't green like Shrek! He was brown, with huge dark eyes that stared at you intently. More than anything, Elvis loved people – especially Jon!

Jon took an apple from the fruit bowl and a carrot from the fridge; although it hadn't been that long since breakfast, Elvis's appetite matched his huge body, so Jon knew he'd be grateful. He was almost out of the kitchen door when he remembered that he was still wearing his baseball cap, and leaned back inside to take it off. It was a nice one, and he didn't want to lose it. Elvis loved eating so much that he really would munch anything in sight. On several occasions he had started to lick his master, raking his giant pink tongue across Jon's head, and had scooped up his hat as well!

Jon strolled over to Elvis's field and the cow immediately came ambling over. He was sometimes so excited to see Jon that he would thunder across the field to say hello, forgetting how big he was, and wouldn't be able to stop. When this happened, Jon had to dive behind a tree to avoid being crushed! But today Elvis seemed to pick up on Jon's mood, knowing he was here to chill out, and moved slowly and carefully.

Or so Jon thought.

Elvis suddenly reached towards him, his big mouth open. Jon smiled, thinking that his cow was going to lick him in a friendly way, but instead, Elvis picked Jon up by the hood of his sweatshirt, leaving his legs dangling above the ground.

"Hey!" Jon called.

Elvis simply stared at him.

"Elvis, cut it out!" he tried again. But the cow just looked at him with mischief in his eyes. It took a lot more shouting from Jon, and then a tap on the nose, before he decided to drop Jon again. He landed on the ground with a thud and stared up at the cow crossly, but Elvis just looked surprised. *What's all this shouting in aid of?* he seemed to be asking. Jon smiled – he could never stay cross with him for long.

Having recovered, Jon scratched Elvis's head and neck, and the cow closed his eyes in delight. He stayed still, chewing away on the food Jon had brought for him, looking thoughtful the whole time.

Jon stayed with Elvis for a while, sometimes talking out loud to him, telling him about the week ahead, and sometimes not, but slowly feeling himself relax. After some time, he stopped stroking Elvis. "Thanks for listening," he told him, and then he headed back to the farmhouse to get on with his day.

CHAPTER THREE

Goating Around

Jon had a helper on the farm called Annie. The animals loved her – and Annie loved them; in fact, she loved all animals more than anybody Jon had ever known. She was always taking care of sick creatures and nursing them back to health. If she ever saw an injured animal she just couldn't resist taking it home to look after.

Jon didn't know what he would do without her. Every morning they would walk the dogs together in the woods and talk about all the things that needed doing on the farm that day, as well as what was going on in their lives.

One morning, a few days after Jon's visit to Elvis, they were walking along talking, the dogs barking happily in front of them, when Annie stopped.

Suddenly realizing that she was no longer beside him, Jon stopped too and went back to where she was standing. "What's wrong?"

"There's nothing wrong with *me*," she told him firmly. "I'm worried about *you*." There was concern and worry in her eyes. "You seem very tired. And you don't seem to be as happy on the farm as you used to."

"I'm fine," Jon insisted. "It's just been a very long, busy summer. I'm feeling a bit weary."

Annie shrugged and said nothing more. But as they made their way back to the farmhouse, Jon couldn't stop thinking about what she had said to him. He had been feeling a little sad lately, but he thought he had been managing to keep it hidden – obviously he was wrong. He flashed back to how much Elvis had cheered him up earlier in the week. *I need to spend more time with the animals I love so much*, he said to himself.

He went into his writing room and sat down at the desk, feeling Izzy curl up at his feet. Suddenly he remembered Annie telling him just a few weeks ago how much fun goats were to have around. More fun sounded good! He knew Annie loved them and had quite a few of her own, so he was sure she would think it was a good idea too.

Jon knew that goats were very friendly and loveable animals, with lots of personality, but that they could also be very, very naughty! The thought of their funny, mischievous faces made him grin. Yes, he decided. He was going to get some goats.

And he opened his computer and started to write an email . . .

★ ★ ★

The very next day, Jon and his friend Maria – and Izzy, of course – drove over to Sandy's farm. Sandy was an old pal who lived nearby, and when Jon had emailed her yesterday telling her he was thinking about getting some goats, she had replied straightaway:

> I've got a couple of baby goats you can have, if you want. Our children raised them, and they've spent lots of time with them. They're friendly but peaceful – you'll love them. Do you want to come over and see them tomorrow?

And so here they were! Sandy's farm was beautiful; it was set on a hillside and was surrounded by green fields – almost picture perfect, Jon thought.

"Hello!" he called as he got out of the car. The whole of Sandy's family were there, smiling as they waited to greet them, and he grinned back – he just knew that the goats were going to be a good addition to Bedlam Farm.

They left Izzy in the car, and Sandy showed Jon and Maria over to the goat pen, letting the babies out when she got there. There were three of them: they pranced about a little, taking careful steps on their awkward legs, showing off in front of these people they'd never seen before. They seemed very confident, but when Jon took a step closer, they stopped in their tracks and looked about nervously before running back inside the pen to be with their mothers. The grown-up goats were quite small too – not even a metre high – but like their babies they had bright, alert eyes that gazed around at everybody.

Jon liked the look of these funny-looking animals very much. As he quietly inspected the goats from a distance, Sandy came over to stand by him, pointing out the two goats that would be his. She told him that the third one, Honey, already had a home on another nearby farm. "You'll love them," she said. "They don't need much room, either."

"What do they like to eat?" asked Jon – knowing how important food was to the other animals of Bedlam Farm.

"Oh, they love nettles, scrubs and weeds – as well as lots of grass and hay."

Jon thought he could manage that! He decided it was time to see what Izzy thought about having these animals as new friends on the farm, so he let the dog out of the car.

Izzy followed Jon confidently, yapping excitedly, pleased to be out in the fresh air, and wagging his black and white tail. He sniffed around at everything, wriggling his little black nose and taking in his surroundings. But it was a totally different matter when the little Border collie got up close to the goat pen!

He simply took one look at the goats prancing about, turned tail and dashed away!

Jon quickly followed to make sure that Izzy didn't run off anywhere dangerous. There was a moment of panic – *where had he gone?* But a flash of shiny eyes gave him away almost immediately – he was hiding under the car! Smelling Jon close by, Izzy poked out first his nose and then the rest of his head to look again – but remembering the goats, he nervously hid away again!

Izzy would have to get used to the new guys on the farm, and Jon knew that he would – he was very friendly. He just had to hope that the goats were too!

Only a few days later, Jon's goats arrived at Bedlam Farm. It was another sunny day when Sandy backed her truck into the driveway, with the baby goats in the back.

Jon had got everything prepared for their arrival and, with Annie's help, was all ready to give the two new animals a home in the back pasture next to the cows.

But when she turned off the engine of her truck, Sandy told Jon she had another idea. "What about putting them in there?" she said.

Jon looked over to where his friend was pointing – at the lambing pen he had in the farm grounds. It had been built when a TV crew came to do some filming on the farm, but Jon had never found a proper use for it. Until now . . .

He saw that the pen would be a perfect spot for the two baby goats. It had a fence around it, so they would be safe, and there were lots of bushes that they could sniff at, eat and play in. He nodded. "Great idea!"

He stood back as Sandy carried the goats over to the pen in her arms, just like human babies. They immediately started exploring on their unsteady legs. She smiled. "Lots to eat, good shelter, rocks and trees. This is perfect – these guys will be very happy here."

* * *

Later that evening Paula and Jon walked out to the pen together, keen to see how the new additions to Bedlam Farm were getting on.

The two little goats were bleating worriedly and their bright eyes looked sad: they were obviously missing their mums. Jon knew he had to make a great home for them here so that they would settle in and be as content as the rest of his animals.

First things first: "What shall we call them?" he said. Naming his animals always felt like the first step to making them feel like they belonged here with him.

Paula thought for a moment. "I'd love it if we named them after my mum and dad – if that's OK with you?"

Jon loved the idea – he liked involving his family in life on the farm, and this was a nice way of doing it. Paula missed her parents just like these little goats were now missing theirs, so it linked them together. And so, Ruth and Murray had arrived!

After the two goats had been at Bedlam for only a few days – getting more settled all the time – Jon had another email from Sandy:

> Dear Jon,
> The other baby goat, Honey, is now missing her brother and sister. We thought we had a home for her, but it's fallen through. Would you take her?

Jon went outside to see Ruth and Murray. They cheerfully bleated hello to him – in fact, it was as if they had always been there. They had lots of scrubland to munch on, Annie and Paula cooing over them and bringing them food – they especially liked leftover popcorn! They were continually chewing on something, but looked thoughtful as they did so. And always, always noisy!

"Shall we bring your sister here, guys?" he asked.

Ruth and Murray gazed back at him.

Jon went back inside. He emailed a response to Sandy:

Sure! Bring Honey over.

CHAPTER FOUR

Feeling Better

One afternoon, not long after Ruth, Murray and Honey had arrived at Bedlam Farm, Jon got a call from a lady he knew only a little called Della. Della's mother, Alice, was very poorly. Alice was one of Jon's neighbours and he liked her very much, though he hadn't seen her for a long time now. She had had her own Border collie for many years, but when she became ill she had to give him away as she couldn't take care of him properly any longer.

"I'm really sorry to disturb you," Della said, "but I've seen you and Izzy around town often, and I know how friendly he is. My mum misses her dog so much. Would you and Izzy maybe be able to pop over and see her some time? I really think it might cheer her up."

Jon hesitated. He liked Alice a lot, and he wanted to help, but he felt nervous. What would he say to her? He didn't know her very well. And what about Izzy? He was a charming and friendly little dog, and he loved meeting new people now, but he'd never been around anybody very poorly before – would he be too much for her to deal with? But, "Of course," he said. How could he say no to Della's request for help?

So the very next day, just after lunch, Jon and Izzy drove over to Alice's house. Della was waiting for them at the door and she gave them a huge, relieved smile. "Thank you so much. Come in, come in." She shook Jon's hand and gave Izzy a friendly pat on the head.

Then she pointed them towards her mother's room.

At first Izzy seemed hesitant about entering the room that Della had indicated. As Jon watched, his dog's eyes darted about, taking in his surroundings and all the new smells. Jon went ahead into the room. Izzy was waiting to be shown what to do, so when Jon beckoned him, he followed obediently, his paws padding along on the wooden floor.

Jon gasped when he saw Alice. She looked much older than she had the last time he had seen her. She was sitting in the corner of the room in a big scruffy armchair, and she appeared very frail and tired. This time it was Jon's turn to hesitate, but as if they had swapped roles, Izzy seemed to know what to do now. He trotted straight over to the old lady, tail wagging, and sat down next to her, resting his head on the arm of her chair.

Immediately the expression on Alice's drawn, pale face changed completely, lit up by a big smile that made her look years younger. She reached out to pat Izzy. Jon smiled as the Border collie stayed completely still while Alice talked to him. "Well, look at you, you handsome boy!" she murmured. "Where have you come from?"

Izzy stared at her intently, as though he understood every word Alice was saying to him.

Jon heard Della turn away from her mother, and when he looked over he saw that she had tears in her eyes. But he was sure they were tears of joy. Alice was obviously delighted to see Izzy: her face was bright with happiness. Jon was very pleased that he and Izzy had come to visit her.

He and Della talked quietly while Alice had her one-sided conversation with Izzy, telling him softly about all sorts of things. But after only about half an hour they realized that Alice's sentences were trailing off and her eyes were closing, so Jon got up to leave.

Izzy didn't need to be called or told what to do. As soon as Jon stood up, he gently rubbed his head against Alice's hand and knee, nuzzling her goodbye, before obediently trotting over to Jon and following him out of the room.

Della followed too, and she grasped Jon's arm tightly before bending to stroke Izzy's head. "Thank you – thank you so much," she said. "You have done Mum the world of good, I know it . . . Do you think we could see you again soon?"

And so Izzy and Jon began going to see Alice every few days, and Jon was more and more proud of his dog: he managed to cheer the old lady up each time he saw her.

But one day they arrived to find Della looking very tired and worried. "I'm afraid Mum can't get out of bed today," she told them sadly.

Jon felt terrible for her; she must have

been exhausting herself with worry about her mother. "Do you want us to come back another time?" he asked, and Izzy rubbed himself against her legs, as if to say, *Don't worry, we're here now.*

"No, please do come in," Della insisted. "I know that she'll still want to see you. She was asking just an hour ago if today was an 'Izzy day'!"

"Stay close, boy," called Jon as they headed towards Alice's room. He was nervous: Izzy was used to meeting Alice when she was in her chair, not in her bed. What if he didn't know what to do?

But, of course, Jon needn't have worried. Izzy adapted immediately, carefully climbing up onto Alice's bed and then gently burrowing his head under the old lady's outstretched hand.

She had been dozing, but, feeling Izzy next to her, she woke up and turned to look at him, smiling her big smile. Jon saw that she was even more drowsy than usual and kept drifting in and out of sleep, sometimes chatting happily to Izzy, sometimes napping again with one hand on his head.

The little dog was very patient, and he seemed to know that it was his job to comfort Alice, and just be around to make her feel better. He lay there quietly, occasionally nuzzling against her but always concentrating on her with his deep brown eyes.

Later, on the way home, Jon starting thinking about what Izzy was managing to do for Alice. His friendly, affectionate little dog had been bringing her so much joy that even when she was so ill she couldn't get out of bed she still wanted to see Izzy and have him near her. Were there other people they could help in this way? he wondered.

"I'm thinking about taking Izzy and volunteering at a hospice," Jon told Paula later that evening. "Izzy has been incredible with Alice and I think we could really help some of the sick people there."

"Are you sure?" Paula asked. "You do have a lot of other responsibilities – you're very busy."

She was right, but during his visits to Alice, Jon had realized that, where he on his own could be awkward, Izzy seemed to know automatically what to do around ill people, and how to cheer them up. They made a good team, and he really thought they could help in some way.

He *was* busy – he was about to start a tour around the country to tell people about the new book he had written, and he had a farm to run too. He knew it would be hard work, but suddenly he really, really wanted to do it.

Jon searched the internet and found a telephone number for the person in charge of organizing volunteers. He made the call with Izzy lying at his feet. He got through to a man called Keith.

Keith seemed very pleased to hear from him, and glad that he wanted to become a volunteer. "But," he warned, "you'll have to go through a lot of training – all our volunteers do."

Jon was surprised by the long list of tasks he would have to complete before he could become a proper volunteer: workshops, homework, trips, training projects . . . But he wasn't put off.

He took a deep breath. "I want to do it. I'll be there next week for my first training session. But there is just one other thing . . . Would you be interested in a volunteer dog?"

Keith was silent.

"I'm serious," Jon insisted. And then he told Keith all about Izzy, his wonderful doggy companion . . .

CHAPTER FIVE

Saying Hello

A week later, Jon and Izzy arrived at the training centre for volunteers. Izzy jumped out of the car and sniffed about eagerly, getting used to the place before turning to look at Jon, waiting to be told what to do. Armed with some fruit and a sandwich for Jon, and some biscuits for Izzy, the pair had arrived for their first training session. They were going to be volunteers.

"This way, boy," Jon told Izzy. As they

headed towards the centre, they attracted a lot of attention. None of the people around had seen a dog in the centre before, and they were all very interested.

Izzy took no notice, and when they were shown into a meeting room, he walked in confidently, his head held high, carefully inspecting all the people.

At the front of the room stood a muscular bald man in a bright polo shirt. His name badge showed him to be KEITH, the man Jon had spoken to on the telephone. Izzy headed straight over to him, knowing without being told that he was the person in charge, and in his usual friendly way put his soft nose in Keith's hand to introduce himself.

"Well, hello there," Keith said cheerfully, looking straight into Izzy's eyes. He turned away for a moment, taking something from the table next to him. Then he held out a name tag for Jon, and one for Izzy too, just as if it were completely normal for him to be meeting a volunteer with four legs instead of two.

With their badges in place, Jon and Izzy took a seat in the middle of the room and got ready to start.

"Welcome to volunteer training," Keith declared as soon as everybody had sat down. He was strict with them right from his first sentence: "There will be no short cuts. We need to make sure that you all know exactly what you're undertaking."

From the moment Keith began speaking there was one trainee volunteer who did not take his eyes off him – Izzy! The little dog was listening intently, his eyes bright and sharp, totally focused on Keith. He was concentrating so hard that Jon almost expected him to pull out a pen and paper and start making notes!

There was so much to take in, and the time flew by, but soon it was time for a quick break. Jon led Izzy outside so that the little dog could stretch his legs and run about – and have a quick wee in the nearby bushes!

When they headed back inside, Keith had kindly set out a bowl of water for Izzy, and the Border collie lapped at it thankfully, his rough pink tongue scooping up the water quickly. That done, Izzy was on the move again! He decided to introduce himself to all the other volunteers on the course.

Just as he had done with Keith, and with

Alice, Izzy padded over to the nearest person – a tall woman with thick black hair – and put his nose on her knee. "Hello there!" she said, surprised.

Hello to you, Izzy smiled with his eyes. And he stayed there for a moment before moving on to the next person. And this is what he did to everybody in the room, approaching them and resting his nose either in their hand or on their knee! Jon smiled – his dog really was the friendliest dog in the world! But what was so great about Izzy, Jon realized – something that would hopefully make him the best as well as the first doggy volunteer – was the way he could judge perfectly how people were feeling. He watched everybody he introduced himself to. If he sensed that they liked him being there, he stayed for a while, nuzzling them and letting them chat to him; if he felt that the person would rather he wasn't there, then he moved on.

★ ★ ★

And their training went well. During the sessions Izzy was always as perfectly behaved and attentive as he had been that first time: he never barked or whined or disturbed anything, and he was friendly and sociable in the breaks, happily munching the biscuits Keith had started to bring for him! And he'd go straight back to work again as soon as the break was over. Jon couldn't help grinning when he saw that his once-wild, frantic dog was now the perfect pupil!

It went well, but it was hard work, just as Jon had been warned. The hours were long, and as well as the work they did in the sessions, Izzy also had to be checked over by a vet to find out whether or not he was the right sort of animal to be around ill people. He passed with flying colours, of course!

But Jon was still nervous. Not only did he have the challenge of preparing *himself* for the hospice work; he also had to get Izzy ready. They would be going to see very, very sick people – who might be hooked up to all sorts of machines – and Jon hoped it wouldn't freak Izzy out. The more he thought about it, the more he realized that Izzy's biggest task was something he could never be trained for – to give love and affection to the people he visited, no matter what their situation. So far, that was something that had come very naturally to the little dog. Jon would just have to keep his fingers crossed that it remained that way.

By the end of the summer they had done it! They had both finished the course and were ready to be volunteers. They had certificates and ID badges. They were all set to go.

Now they just had to see what and where their first job together would be.

And it wasn't long before they found out.

One muggy, late-summer afternoon, Jon and Izzy drove to meet the first person they had been assigned to, an eighty-six-year-old woman called Jamie, who was very ill indeed. Jamie had been a dog-lover all her life, and so her carers had thought that Jon – and Izzy, of course – would be a perfect match for her.

When they arrived, Jamie's daughter, Carol, was waiting for them. She was short and slim, with a friendly round face, but there were huge bags under her tired eyes and it was obvious that she was worn out with taking care of her mother. "It's so great to have you here," she told them. "My mum loved her own dogs so much. She'll be very happy to see Izzy."

Jon washed his hands in the bathroom while Izzy waited patiently by the door, and then Carol led them towards her mother's room. "Is she watching the TV?" Jon asked, hearing the murmur of voices from the room.

"No," answered Carol, "probably not, but I like to leave it on low for her so that she never feels like she's totally on her own."

Jon and Izzy both took in Jamie's room when they entered. It was pretty and tidy, and filled with family photographs and flowers. And there, lying in bed in the middle of the room, was Jamie. She was a beautiful lady and, because Jon and Izzy had come to visit, Carol had painted her mother's nails and put some lipstick on her.

"Mama? This is Izzy," she said loudly and slowly. "And Jon. They've come to see you."

The old lady's eyes didn't move. She was just staring into space.

Because this was Jon and Izzy's first visit as proper volunteers, Keith, their trainer, had come along to watch so that he could check how they did. Right now he looked on nervously, hoping that Jon and his first ever dog volunteer would do a good job.

"Izzy is just like Flash, isn't he?" Carol tried again to get her mother's attention.

Jon moved near to the end of Jamie's bed,

looked at Izzy and then gestured for the Border collie to climb up.

Izzy did so as gently as he could.

"Stay," instructed Jon.

Obedient as ever, Izzy sat stock-still at the foot of Jamie's bed, but though his body was still, his mind was obviously working quickly, taking in everything. He looked around, his pointy ears and fluffy tail upright. He cocked his head at Jon. *What shall I do?* he seemed to be asking.

"It's OK, Iz," Jon told him. "You can say hello."

So Izzy did just that. As Jon and Keith and Carol watched, he lay down and started slowly inching his way up the side of the bed.

For a moment Jon panicked. Was this the right thing for Izzy to be doing? Would he frighten Jamie, or would she frighten him? But Izzy didn't step on Jamie or even graze her frail body. When he got close to her hand, he burrowed his head underneath it and lay still, staring at her intently.

And then, to Jon's delight, Jamie realized that Izzy was there. At first she was fearful, and her shoulders seemed to tense, but then she smiled. She didn't look at Izzy, but moved her hand slightly, running her fingers through the fur on his head and ears. "Oh," she said, her voice cracking. "Oh, how pretty."

"This is the first time she's spoken in weeks!" Carol was overjoyed.

Jon and Keith grinned, but held their breath, waiting to see what would happen next.

Izzy lay still while Jamie stroked him, mumbling to him occasionally, and after a while she drifted peacefully off to sleep – still smiling. Izzy stayed in the same position at Jamie's side for about fifteen more minutes before, without any instruction from Jon, he plopped down gracefully from the bed and padded over to Carol. He gazed at her with his big brown eyes and held out his paw to her.

Izzy Katz, the doggy volunteer, had completed his first job successfully.

"Thank you," whispered Carol.

As they left quietly a little later, Keith shook Jon's hand and patted Izzy cheerfully. "This is awesome. It works," he said, smiling. "Izzy is a natural – and you aren't so bad yourself."

CHAPTER SIX

A New Litter

And so, with the addition of their volunteer work, life for Jon and Izzy was busier than ever. But little did they know that things were going to get even more hectic – and the challenge would come in the form of a very cute, very hungry four-legged friend!

Jon had some good friends called Gretchen and John. They had been breeding dogs for a long time and Jon loved seeing them

– and their dogs – and he, Rose and Izzy would often spend time with them.

One day Jon got an email from them inviting him to come over to say hello to their new puppies.

One of our girls has had a new litter,

Gretchen said.

Jon didn't want a new dog, but he loved seeing new puppies with their mothers – and he wanted to see Gretchen and John, so he told her he'd see them soon.

Later that day he was introduced to the puppies – and there were lots of them: little Labrador retrievers, all tiny and squashed up, with wrinkly faces, nudging and shoving each other out of the way, yapping and blinking their little eyes. Jon stood over them, grinning as they played about, slowly getting used to their little stubby legs. And then one of them caught his attention.

She was a little girl, jet-black and pudgy – and very cute! As Jon watched, she marched right through the middle of a tub of mushed-up dog food, gulping down bits of it as she went. Mid-mouthful, she looked up and caught Jon staring at her. Immediately her alert eyes focused on him. *Who are you?* she seemed to be asking. She had a spark of attitude in her eyes – they were full of mischief, and Jon liked that! The puppy looked at him for just a little longer, and then yawned, wagged her tail and went back to her dinner. Jon knew from caring for Pearl and Clementine that Labradors loved eating, and this puppy was obviously no exception!

Even though she was only a baby, Jon could tell that she would grow up to be a beautiful dog – she was certainly cute enough now! She had a perfectly shaped head and body, and her coat and eyes were glossy. Jon couldn't drag his eyes away from her. The puppy's brothers and sisters rolled over each other and threw themselves against the fence, trying to get Jon's attention, but this little girl Labrador didn't. She would look over at him every now and then. *You're quite interesting, I suppose*, she seemed to be saying. *But my food is better!*

Jon was hooked!

"I think I could manage one more dog on—" he started to say, and then he stopped himself. He had just been saying how busy he was, how much he had going on – he shouldn't be thinking about getting another dog . . . But she was so cute! In spite of himself, Jon kept looking back at the glossy little black bundle in front of him and thinking how well she would fit in on Bedlam Farm. With Pearl and Clementine both living with other people, and Rose and Izzy as settled and happy as they'd ever be, he was sure he could manage one more dog on the farm. He suddenly liked the idea of a dog who could do a little bit of work around the farm, but would more importantly be a friend, keep him company. He really wanted this dog.

Gretchen appeared to know exactly what he was thinking. "Why don't you come back and see her again in a few days?" she suggested. "See how you feel then."

Jon nodded. "I'll bring Rose and Izzy, if that's OK?" he said. He knew he couldn't rush into this: it was a big decision and he needed to know that this dog would fit in well on his farm and into his life.

"Of course." Gretchen completely understood. "See you very soon."

On the drive home, Jon couldn't get the puppy out of his head. A name for her came to him immediately – Lenore. It was the title of a poem by one of his favourite writers, and he thought it suited her perfectly. There was still some doubt in his mind, though. Taking on a puppy was a big commitment – was he ready for it again?

★ ★ ★

That evening, Jon decided to ring Paula and see what she thought. After talking about their days for a while, Jon said, "Honey, I've met a puppy."

"OK . . ." Paula was hesitant. "Tell me about her."

And Jon did, finding himself smiling as he described the little Labrador's appearance and mischievous charm.

"You've already thought of a name, haven't you?" Paula asked, sounding resigned.

Jon had to admit that he had. "Lenore – after that poem I love."

Paula sighed. "It sounds to me like you've made up your mind. When you name a puppy, you've already decided you want it."

And Jon realized that his wife was right. He had, and he did!

CHAPTER SEVEN

Meet Lenore

Jon returned to Gretchen and John's just a couple of days later, taking Rose and Izzy with him as he had said he would.

Jon asked his dogs to wait by the gate, and then Gretchen led him over to the puppy pen and scooped a hand in, pulling out Jon's favourite from the wriggling mass of her brothers and sisters.

"Hello, Lenore," Jon whispered. "How are you, girl?"

Gretchen smiled. "Lenore? Nice name."

Jon smiled too. She was just as beautiful as he remembered. He was excited; now he wanted to know what the two animals he currently loved best thought of their potential playmate.

He called Rose and Izzy over. "This is Lenore, guys. Say hello!"

But to his disappointment, they didn't really seem that bothered about her at all! Rose stood to one side, suspiciously eyeing up this tiny little creature. Izzy was a little more forthcoming and moved over to sniff her. But Lenore's smell obviously didn't interest him one bit: he ignored her totally and went off to follow other scents. Rose did the same: she inspected Lenore, getting her scent, before moving away, clearly bored.

Jon was sad to see that they hadn't immediately made friends – the perfect scene he'd pictured, with them all playing together, hadn't happened – but at least they hadn't hated each other. Lenore didn't seem that interested in Rose and Izzy, either! He had brought some puppy treats with him and he held one out now. Lenore took it from Jon's hand gratefully, and stayed just long enough for him to pat her on the head before trotting back towards her family. Maybe he had got too excited, Jon thought to himself.

But he decided to try again. Lenore was still too young to leave her mother anyway, and he couldn't help but think they would make a perfect team. Though the goats had cheered him up a lot, he still felt sad sometimes, and the prospect of having her in his life had been making him feel much more positive. He couldn't say no to her now.

And he was so glad he hadn't done so.

The next time he went to visit her at Gretchen and John's, things were totally different!

Lenore recognized him straightaway, and

came over to the fence of her pen as soon as she spotted him, her mischievous eyes gleaming and her stumpy tail wagging happily. Jon felt all warm inside.

"She likes you," Gretchen whispered. She scooped up the little puppy and placed her in Jon's lap.

Jon held his breath. He'd only gone so far as to pat Lenore before. How would she take to this?

Brilliantly! She snuggled up on Jon's knees as if they were a cosy bed, and leaned her head against his chest.

Jon looked at her, and as she raised her eyes to meet his, they twinkled – she seemed to be smiling. Then she nestled down even further on his lap and went straight to sleep.

Gretchen stood by, watching closely. "After reading your books," she said softly, "I knew you'd like this one. She's sweet and calm, and she's going to be beautiful. You'll get on perfectly."

Jon glanced again at the snoozing bundle of black fur in his arms and smiled. He could already tell that Gretchen was right.

There was lots to get ready before he could bring Lenore home to Bedlam Farm. He went to the pet shop and bought a crate for her to sleep in, bags of treats, a tiny collar – and, because he'd had Labrador puppies before, some odour repellent and disinfectant. They could be very messy.

He was very excited. He loved Rose and Izzy more than anything, but Labradors were, hands down, his favourite breed of dog. He did some reading up on them just to remind himself of a few things. He knew how important it was to be prepared.

LABRADOR RETRIEVERS

- Labrador retrievers are a type of gun dog, used to retrieve (bring back) birds and animals shot for sport, but they make excellent pets and are one of the most popular breeds of dog in the world.

- They were first bred on the island of Newfoundland in Canada and were used by fishermen to help with pulling nets in from the water – the dog swims out and grabs the floating corks on the end of the nets and brings them in.

- They are quite big dogs. An average male weighs 30–36 kg. They love eating so they sometimes eat too much and get a bit too fat.

- Their coats are usually either black, yellow or what is called chocolate (medium to dark brown).

- Their coats are water-repellent so they don't get cold if they go in the water in the winter. They also have webbed toes so they are great swimmers.

- They are gentle, clever, good-natured dogs and are particularly good with children.

- They have very soft mouths – a Labrador can carry an egg in its mouth without breaking it!

And soon the day came when Lenore was ready to leave her mother. Jon drove over to pick her up from Gretchen's, a smile on his face the whole way there.

"Hello, little lady," he said, pulling her onto his lap again when he arrived. Lenore looked at him cheekily, and started softly gnawing on Jon's chin – she left lots of slobber behind! "I want you to be calm and easy. I want you to go places with me," he told her seriously. "But I don't want you running off. OK?"

Lenore stopped chewing. She looked Jon right in the eye and licked him carefully with her soft pink tongue. *OK*, she seemed to be saying. *You've got yourself a deal. I'm ready to come home.*

Jon really thought she had understood him perfectly. He couldn't wait to have her in his life.

CHAPTER EIGHT

Trouble at Bedtime

The journey back to Bedlam Farm was straightforward. Lenore was quiet, and although she must have been a little nervous, the cheeky glint in her eye made Jon think that she was tough, that she would be OK.

Rose and Izzy were out walking with Annie, so when Jon and Lenore arrived home, he put the puppy's brand-new shiny little collar and lead on her and got ready to show her around the farm. "This is it, girl, your new home! I hope you like it."

Lenore kept very close to Jon's side as they went to meet her farm-mates, her dark eyes darting about as she moved like Jon's shadow on her pudgy little legs. *Yap! Yap-yap!* she said cheerfully when she met each new animal – just as if she were introducing herself to them all. And every time she did it, Jon smiled – he was totally besotted with her.

But not all the residents of Bedlam Farm were as happy to meet her as Jon had been. Hearing and smelling Jon coming, the donkeys brayed loudly and rushed over to meet him as usual, hoping for a treat. Jon tensed, thinking that these big, smelly creatures would scare little Lenore – but he was wrong. It was the other way round! *Yap! Yap-yap!* she cried. *Hello! Nice to meet you!* And she pushed her squidgy little nose against the side of their pen. Lulu, Jeanette, Fanny and Jesus didn't like it at all. *Who is this strange, cheeky thing?* they seemed to be asking, and they lowered their ears and backed away from her.

The same thing happened with the goats – as soon as Lenore came near and yapped at them, Ruth, Murray and Honey took off to the other side of their pen. And then Mother and Minnie, the farm cats, also disappeared as soon as she came in sight.

Lenore wasn't put off, still barking happily, her eyes bright, so Jon decided to carry on with her tour of the farm. Elvis was next, and the two of them headed over to his field. The big cow was so kind and gentle that Jon was sure he'd love this little newcomer, and Lenore hadn't seemed fazed so far. But when they arrived, he panicked.

Lenore boldly rushed over to Elvis's field, her tail wagging, yapping as loudly as she could. Elvis ambled over to investigate.

Jon looked up at the big old cow coming towards them, and then down at the tiny little puppy at his side, and he tugged on Lenore's lead to bring her closer to him. The size difference between these two animals was huge. Would Lenore be scared? he wondered.

She didn't seem to be!

Elvis finally reached the fence surrounding his field and looked Lenore up and down thoughtfully.

Jon held his breath.

Elvis lowered his head and opened his mouth just a little. And then let out the hugest sneeze Jon had ever seen or heard! *Aaaa-chhhh-oooo!*

Jon looked down and saw that Lenore was covered from head to toe in Elvis's spit and gloop! He bent down to pick up her in his arms. "It's OK—" he started to say.

But Lenore wriggled away from him and pushed herself back up against the fence. Then she stuck out her little pink tongue and licked Elvis on the nose. That was it! Covered in

You might like these photographs of Jon's dogs and the animals of Bedlam Farm.

Enjoy looking through them!

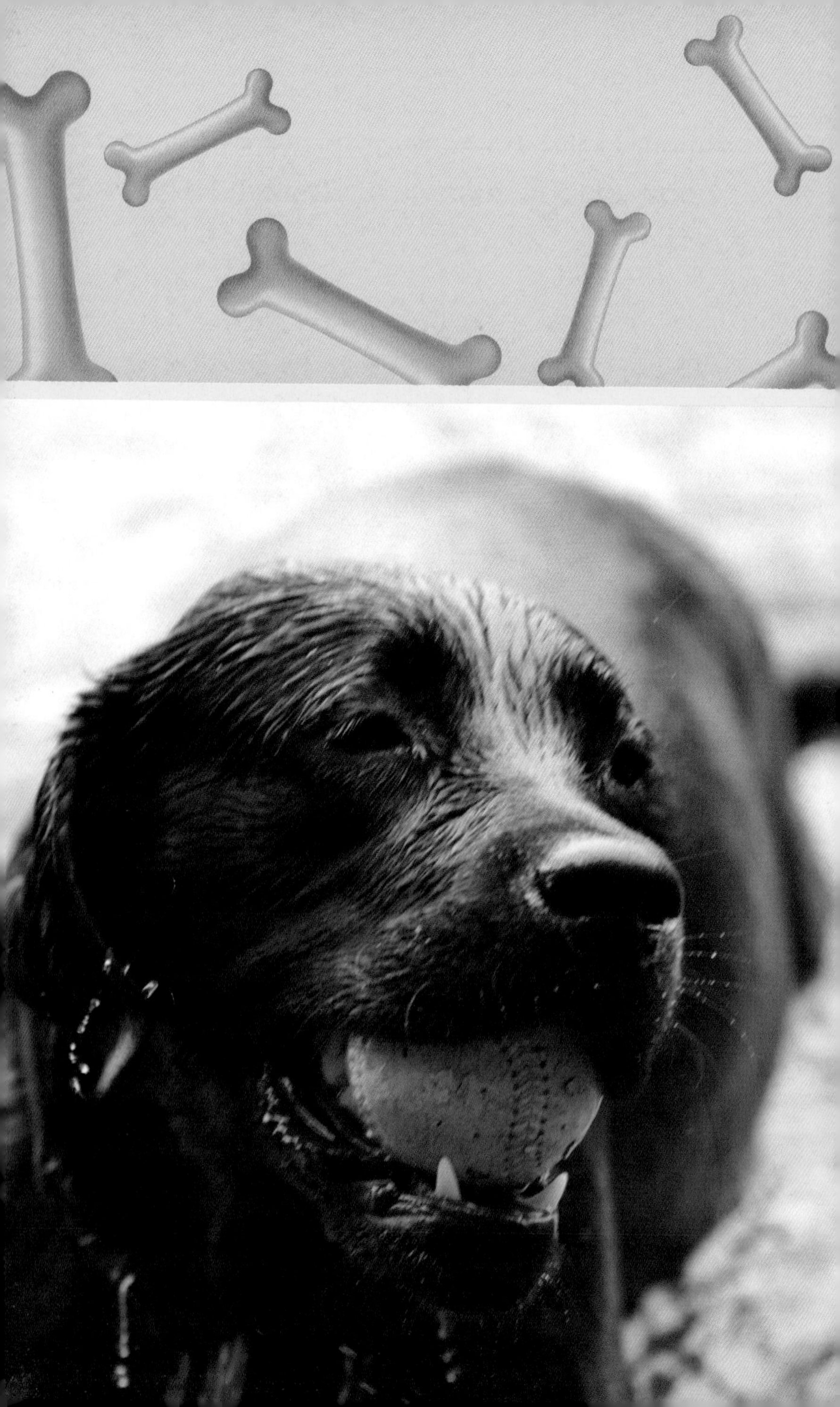

cow gloop or not, Lenore had made her first friend on the farm!

That night, when he had done all his evening chores, Jon settled down on the sofa to read a book. He gently picked up Lenore and tucked her next to him. She nestled against him happily. Jon felt very peaceful. He had done the right thing in bringing Lenore here, he was certain.

But the peace was very soon shattered!

An hour or so later, at bedtime, Jon led Lenore into the kitchen, where he had set out her sleeping crate with some warm blankets inside. "In here, little lady. In here." Jon beckoned her into the crate, and she padded in happily, exploring the new space, foraging about with her nose.

That was easy, he thought.

Too soon! As he started to back away towards the kitchen door to go to his own bed, Lenore started to whine softly. She hadn't been away from Jon's side all day, and now she was scared.

Jon felt terrible, but he knew that this was for the best. They had to get into a sleeping routine as soon as they could, and the crate was a good way to do it. He kept moving away until he reached the door, and then he went out and shut it firmly behind him.

Lenore's whines just got louder and louder, and all the way up the stairs he could hear her shrieking and howling for him. This was awful, he knew, but he *had* to be firm. Lenore was safe in the kitchen; she was just shocked at being left alone in new surroundings. So he gritted his teeth and got himself ready for bed.

A little while later – the terrible noise from the kitchen still going on – Jon heard his bedroom door creak open. Thinking that little Lenore had somehow managed to escape from her crate and the kitchen, he sat bolt upright in bed. But it wasn't Lenore; it was

Rose and Izzy, their black noses appearing round his door before the rest of their bodies followed. They barked loudly over the sound of Lenore. *Can we stay up here with you?* they seemed to be saying. *We can't stand the noise!*

They spent the rest of the night under Jon's bed!

The next night Jon tried leaving Lenore in the crate again. He had done this with Devon and Izzy, and all his other dogs, and though he hated to hear his little puppy whining, he knew how important it was that he stood his ground. The other dogs had all grown to love their cosy crates.

But when Jon led her into the crate, clever little Lenore now knew what was coming up and refused to go all the way inside, stubbornly leaving either her bottom or her nose sticking out. Jon had tried to make the crate feel like a nice safe place for the puppy to sleep, filling it with treats and chews that Lenore would like, but it wasn't working at all.

This time, when he had finally coaxed her inside, left her and shut the door behind him, she did whine for a while, but it was nowhere near as loud as the night before, and it ended sooner – with Rose and Izzy able to sleep without having to hide under Jon's bed!

The next day, Jon fed Lenore her breakfast in the crate, trying to make it seem like a nice place to be, and by that night – her third – the clever little puppy had realized that her sleeping place was actually cosy and comfortable and that she didn't need to be scared at all. She snuggled down happily and slept the whole night through, and when Jon came down to see her the following morning he could hear her little doggy snores before he had even opened the kitchen door!

CHAPTER NINE

Izzy Works His Magic

After that, things got better for Lenore every day. She was happy on Bedlam Farm, always cheery and dashing about on her short little legs. Paula, Annie and Emma loved her – and so did everybody who met her. She was hard to resist, and just so cute! Whenever Jon took her with him to run errands in the nearby town, people stopped and said things like, "How adorable!" "Look at that gorgeous puppy!" And the couple who ran the post office always wanted a cuddle and a kiss from her!

Though Rose and Izzy didn't love her the way they loved each other, they all lived together very happily. Lenore was very stubborn: she never stopped trying to make them be her friends – her eyes followed them around the room and she would gnaw on their ruffs and give them friendly licks, hoping to get them to play with her. Rose and Izzy would look at each other, and Jon could almost imagine them rolling their eyes and saying, *Who on earth is this little thing?*

The other animals on the farm quickly became less suspicious of her too. The goats stopped to watch her dashing about rather than backing away, and even came over to say hello. The cats no longer fled from her, and even Winston the rooster just carried on pecking away as normal, letting the new puppy run around him manically if she wanted to!

★ ★ ★

The summer ended and the nights were getting colder. Jon and Izzy returned one evening after visiting a lady called Etta who lived in a nursing home. It was getting dark when they got back to Bedlam Farm, and Jon was tired and hungry and desperate to get in out of the cold.

As soon as they entered the house, Lenore rushed over to them, barking excitedly. Her eyes were gleaming, and she was so excited her little legs could barely keep up with her! She ran around Jon, and then Izzy, and then back again, rubbing herself against Jon and stopping occasionally to give Izzy a friendly sniff.

Jon bent down and scooped her up into his arms. She snuggled closer, giving him a hello lick. Jon's mood lifted immediately: just knowing that this little creature was there at home, longing to see him again, always cheered him up – and it did so now. "Hello there, girl!" he said happily.

Lenore had calmed down now that Jon had her in his arms; she kept nuzzling into his chest. He looked down at her and couldn't stop a smile spreading over his face.

Later that evening, when it was bedtime, Jon picked Lenore up off the sofa where she'd been snuggling next to him as usual, and carried her over to her crate in the kitchen. He was pleased he'd been strict with her during her first couple of days at the farm – now there were never any problems with bedtimes.

"Crate," he said now, and tossed in one of her favourite toys. Lenore padded inside as obediently as always, but Jon noticed that she was walking more slowly than usual. Once he had shut her in, she pressed her little head against the gate, gazing up at him with those big dark eyes. She was making Jon feel very guilty!

"I'm sorry, little lady," he said, "but you know the rules. You have to sleep in there."

But tonight he felt even guiltier than normal as he walked towards the kitchen door.

He turned back to look at her and thought he saw her shiver. Lenore made a little yelping noise, as if she were saying, *It's so cold down here – don't leave me!* and he just couldn't resist her. He went back to the crate and took her out, carrying her upstairs to his bedroom.

Jon brushed his teeth and put on his pyjamas, and when he came back, there she was, cosily settled on one of his pillows, breathing heavily and peacefully. She wriggled about when Jon got into the bed, and moved across to curl up at his side. And there, like a little hot-water bottle, she slept cosily all night long.

The next night she slept in the same place. And the next, and the next. In fact, Lenore never slept in her crate again!

The time flew by, with Jon enjoying Lenore's company in the day – as well as at night! He was very glad that he had gone to say hello to John and Gretchen's litter on that sunny day.

He and Izzy were often busy with their hospice work now. During their training, they had always been told to expect the unexpected – which was what they faced one day that winter.

Jon was told that he and Izzy would be going to see a man called Harry, who had been a teacher. He and his wife, Edra, had owned their own farm and he loved animals – especially Border collies who herded sheep like Izzy and Rose. The hospice thought that Harry would have lots in common with Jon and Izzy, so they had arranged a meeting.

On the way over, Jon thought about the visit. Up till now, the people he and Izzy had seen had lived very different lives to his; it was strange to be visiting somebody who was not only his age, but who also had so much in common with him. He looked over at

Izzy in the passenger seat: the little dog was gazing out of the window thoughtfully, and Jon wondered whether he was thinking about the job that lay ahead.

Jon took a deep breath. He knew that he and Izzy could only do their best. They would just have to use their judgement with Harry – Izzy was great at that, after all.

When they got to Harry's house, Jon gasped – it was absolutely beautiful: a lovely wood cabin surrounded by gorgeous hills and fields. The inside was just as nice – very warm and homely.

Edra showed them to her husband's room. Harry was sitting listening to his iPod under a blanket. Jon couldn't help smiling – Harry was wearing his trainers with his dressing gown! His room was filled with books and magazine and baseball stuff – he was certainly very different to the other ill people Jon and Izzy had visited before.

Izzy seemed surprised too, and instead of

following Jon into Harry's room, he waited by the door.

"Hello!" Harry said cheerfully. Except for the dressing gown and the pallor of his face, you would have had no idea he was so sick.

As soon as he had spoken, Izzy seemed to know just what to do, as usual. Jon watched as his dog padded over and rested his head on Harry's knee – his normal greeting.

Harry smiled. "So you're the famous Izzy all the hospice people are talking about," he said, stroking the little dog's head. "I'm very pleased to meet you."

Izzy barked. *Very nice to meet you too.*

Jon grinned – he knew Izzy was becoming well-known; he'd even had his photo in the paper for being the first dog to do the hospice training. The nurses all loved him and talked about him a lot, and everybody who met him realized how well he was managing to connect with the patients. But it was nice to know that the people they visited had all heard good things about him too.

Harry and Jon talked for a few minutes, with Jon telling him about Bedlam Farm and hearing about Harry's life. At first Izzy stayed completely still, his head on Harry's knee. After a little while, though, he climbed up onto the sofa next to Harry, lay down and put his head on his lap.

Harry stopped speaking, surprised. "You are a sweetheart, aren't you?" he said, and then he turned away from Jon and began mumbling to the dog and playing with his ears and paws.

As Jon watched them together, he realized that one of the great things about Izzy was that he loved people so easily – no matter who they were or what they did.

And this was certainly the case with Harry. He and Izzy were soon sitting snuggled up together as if they'd been friends for years, Harry peacefully rubbing the dog's soft fur.

Before long Izzy dozed off on Harry's lap. Harry snoozed too.

Jon just sat and watched, happy that yet again Izzy had managed to work his magic.

CHAPTER TEN

The Part-time Dog

It wasn't long before Jon and Izzy had to work their magic again – again for somebody completely unexpected. Only a week or so later, it was time for them to meet Timmy.

Timmy was only seven years old, but he was very poorly indeed and had to stay in bed a lot of the time.

Marla, his mum, looked tired and worried. "Timmy loves dogs," she told Jon when he and Izzy arrived at their house. "He used to have a golden retriever called Ginger, but she died unfortunately. It's very sad – he really misses her."

When they got to Timmy's room, the door was ajar and Jon could see that the little boy was watching a Disney film. He hesitated and took a deep breath. Would this be OK? he wondered. His daughter, Emma, was all grown up now, and neither he nor Izzy spent much time around young people.

Izzy stood in the doorway and inspected the room, his eyes taking in everything around him. He quickly spotted the boy in bed and looked him up and down.

Timmy had dark eyes and wavy brown hair. His bedside table was covered with colourful toys and books and cards.

"Timmy!" his mum called, trying to distract her son from the film he was glued to. "Here's a dog called Izzy. He's come to see you."

Timmy pressed PAUSE on the remote

control, and turned to them. A smile lit up his little face.

Immediately Izzy padded over to Timmy's bed and sat beside it, gazing up at him. The little dog looked very professional and serious, perfectly poised, but he didn't do anything: he wasn't yet sure whether he should jump up and say hello; he was just taking things in, slowly figuring out what was best.

"Marla?" Jon asked Timmy's mum. "Do you think we should introduce Timmy and Izzy properly now?"

She nodded, smiled, and she and Jon moved closer to Timmy's bed.

Jon gave Izzy the "up" command with his hand, and immediately Izzy hopped onto the end of the bed. He lay down at first, and Jon knew he was trying not to scare the little boy. Then he slowly moved up the bed towards Timmy, until he was close enough to rest his head on his shoulder.

"Hey!" The little boy smiled, showing his

teeth – there were a few missing! "Are you my new dog?"

Jon felt a pang inside, and wished he could find Timmy a dog who would make him as happy as Izzy made him. "Izzy can sort of be your dog," he told the little boy. "He lives on the farm with me, but he's going to come and visit you a lot – he'll be like your part-time dog."

Timmy looked sad. "Can't he stay here? *Please*, can't I keep him?"

"I'm sorry." Jon wondered if bringing Izzy here had been the right thing to do. Maybe not being allowed to have Izzy with him the whole time would make things worse for Timmy. "We'll come and see you whenever you want us to," he told the boy. "But Izzy has a home with all the other animals on the farm. They would really miss him if he wasn't there any more. I promise he'll come by and visit all the time, though."

Timmy looked a little confused; he wasn't

sure how this would work. So Jon tried explaining another way: "You'll get to have all the fun times with Izzy and do all the great stuff like playing, and I'll do the things like walking and feeding him."

It seemed to work. Timmy thought for a moment, and then nodded contentedly. "That seems like a good deal." He moved his little hand to rub the fur on Izzy's head and back. "What other animals do you have on the farm?" he asked Jon.

As Jon told him about Rose and Lenore, Elvis and Luna, and all the donkeys, goats and chickens at Bedlam Farm, Timmy sat, fascinated, stroking Izzy the whole time.

Suddenly Izzy wriggled round and rested his head on Timmy's chest. "Hey," the little boy said to his mum. "Izzy is awesome!"

Jon could see that Izzy and Timmy were going to be great friends.

For the next half-hour, Timmy bombarded Jon with questions about Izzy: "Where did

Izzy come from? . . . Did you name him?" and so on.

Jon told Timmy as much as he could, and when the little boy finally stopped for breath, his mum put her hand on Jon's arm and smiled. "Timmy's looking and sounding better than he has for weeks!" she said happily.

Once again, Jon was filled with pride at what his clever little dog could do for people. They always seemed so much happier after spending time with Izzy.

Izzy lay on the bed with Timmy for a while longer before hopping down to join Jon again. Jon was deep in thought, and jumped when he felt Izzy rubbing against his leg. He wondered if there was a problem, but when he looked up, he realized that Timmy's eyes had closed and he was falling asleep. Izzy had known just what to do, of course!

Leaving Timmy to sleep, Jon and Izzy went to find his mum. "How great of you to come," she said as she got up to show them out. "Izzy really cheered Timmy up. Thank you so very much."

Jon whispered goodbye to Timmy and started to head for the door, but Izzy stayed where he was, staring at the boy for a long time before moving over to join Jon. It was as though he wanted to watch over Timmy and make sure he was safe before they left.

"I think we'll be back," Jon said.

And they *were* back.

From then on, Jon and Izzy returned to see Timmy every few days. And Jon took him some photos of Izzy, so that even when they weren't there, Timmy could still see the dog. He pinned them up on the wall by his bed.

As soon as they arrived, Izzy would snuggle up close next to the little boy and they'd have a chat. Timmy would stroke Izzy before they both fell asleep, happy and contented.

CHAPTER ELEVEN

It's Bedtime!

With his visits to Timmy, as well as to Harry and lots of other people, with Lenore, the farm and his books, Jon had a lot going on. But there were still times when he felt sad and lonely. He missed Paula and Emma. They did love the farm, so they came to visit a lot, but Paula was a teacher in New York and Emma was busy writing a book – just like her dad!

Thanks to the animals of Bedlam Farm, though, Jon was never alone. No matter what kind of day it was, the farm carried on as normal; the animals mooed and baaed and brayed just as they always did. Whenever Jon came near, Lenore yapped excitedly, her eyes widening and her tail wagging. She would tumble over in her excitement to get to him, and Jon loved it.

Whenever he was feeling down, it was Rose who seemed to sense his mood. There were occasions when she would not leave Jon's side, and even started sleeping with him and Lenore. Normally she liked to have her own space at night-time, so that she could get up and go to the window to check that the sheep were still behaving themselves! But when she sensed that Jon wasn't himself, she would snuggle up to him whenever and wherever she could, resting her soft head on his lap and gazing up at him with her thoughtful eyes to try and give him some comfort. He often tried to hide the fact that he was feeling sad, but then he'd suddenly see that Rose had come to lie next to him on the sofa, or was at his feet while he was writing, or hadn't left his side while they were walking, and he'd realize that she knew something was wrong – she knew him better than all the other animals on Bedlam Farm. He was very lucky to have her in his life. "You know something's up, don't you, girl?" Jon said to her.

Rose looked at him with her alert eyes. *Yes*, she seemed to be saying. *And I wish I could help*.

Jon knew she already was helping.

And so did the other animals. Jon's daily routine was full of them, and he made sure he had time for them all, no matter how he was feeling. He especially set aside lots of time for Lenore, keeping up her training and making sure that they got to know each other properly. They also had lots of cuddles. It was still early days, and he wanted to make sure she was getting the best start to her life on the farm.

And things were going well: Lenore had settled down and seemed to like her busy daily routine.

One night, though, she made Jon very worried!

They had been snuggled on the sofa together, and he'd dozed off in front of the TV. When he woke up, he rubbed his eyes sleepily and reached down to pat Lenore. But she wasn't there!

He put on his glasses and called her name over and over again, searching the house for her. "Lenore! Here, girl!" he shouted into all the rooms. But there was no sign of her. Jon glanced at the clock: nine-thirty – it was dark now. Surely she couldn't have gone wandering off outside somewhere? *Where was she?* Jon panicked, furious with himself for dozing off. Since arriving on the farm, Lenore had never strayed far from his side. *Where could she be?* He quickly found a torch and, without stopping to put on a coat, headed outside. He shone the light into every nook and cranny he could think of, calling her name again and again, but there was no sign of her.

Then he decided to shout for Rose. She could have been a brilliant search-and-rescue dog, and he had often called upon her to help him find Izzy when he'd first come to the farm and was always running away! She would know what to do, he was sure. But as he rushed back to the farmhouse, something made him decide to search in all the rooms one more time.

Jon headed up the stairs and suddenly realized that there was one room he hadn't looked in. He went into his bedroom.

And there, curled up in a little black ball on the floor, was Lenore, fast asleep. Jon wanted to sink to his knees in relief. He rushed over to her and scooped her up, putting one hand under her bottom. "Well, hi, sweetie!" he said to her. "Have you been here all along? Aren't I stupid!" She awoke, turning her drowsy, confused face to him. *What are you panicking about?* she seemed to be saying. *It's bedtime.* And as she stared up at him with her sleepy little black eyes, he realized he had been very silly. All that had happened was that Lenore had been ready for bed. She had obviously padded upstairs to wait for Jon, but she was too small to jump up onto his bed without his help. So now here she was, asleep on the floor.

Happy that Jon had finally come to join her, she wagged her stumpy tail, licked his face a bit and then fell asleep again in his arms. Jon laid her on one of the pillows, and she was snoring before he had even left the room.

Despite himself, Jon grinned. This little dog could make herself comfortable anywhere! It was bedtime, so here she was – just where she'd been all along!

Although he had been so worried by the thought of Lenore going off alone somewhere, Jon couldn't bring himself to shout at her – and this was always the way. She was so cute that he really found it hard to be as strict with her as he was with Rose and Izzy.

Part of the reason, he realized, was that just as Izzy cheered up the ill people he visited, Lenore helped Jon in the same way. With her around, always curious, playful and alert, it was hard to be sad or grumpy, and Jon was finding that he was feeling sad and lonely more and more rarely. She constantly reminded him of why he loved dogs so much. This very cute one in particular!

CHAPTER TWELVE

The Hungriest Dog in the World

Cute she might be, but when it came to food, Lenore could also be very naughty! In her first few months on Bedlam Farm she ate all sorts of gross stuff that Jon just couldn't believe:

- chicken droppings;
- dead things in the woods;
- biros;
- socks;
- twigs.

You name it, Lenore would eat it – she must be the hungriest dog in the world, Jon thought. She would lie in front of Rose and Izzy while they were eating so that as soon as they moved away, she could tuck in, polishing off their leftovers. Whenever Jon came into the kitchen, she was there in a flash, waiting to see if there was a treat for her somewhere. If something fell on the floor, no matter what it was, it would be gone, lapped up by her pink tongue, quicker than you could blink.

One day Jon was in the kitchen making himself some lunch – Lenore was there too, of course, sniffing about for something to munch – when he accidentally knocked a whole box of eggs onto the kitchen floor.

"Oh, no!" he cried. They had splattered all over the place. He went to the sink to get a cloth to start wiping up the mess – but when he turned back, he couldn't believe his eyes!

Lenore had very quickly realized that this

mess on the floor was food. And she was beside herself! She had obviously rolled in all the egg goo as well as walked in it. There were eggy footprints all over the kitchen, and she was covered in yellow gloop and bits of shell. As for the mess on the floor, well, it was almost completely gone! Lenore had licked up every single bit of egg.

"Lenore!" Jon exclaimed. And she looked up at him with bright eyes, full of mischief – she had enjoyed that!

Jon reached out for her so that she didn't tread eggy prints all over the rest of the house. She was smelly and very sticky. There was nothing for it! He scooped her up in his arms, covering his jumper with egg. It was time for a doggy bath!

Only a few days later, Lenore showed her love of food again!

Jon had recently become very interested in photography; he was getting better and better at it. It was a lovely, clear, crisp day – great for taking pictures – and so he decided to head into the nearby town with his camera.

When he put on his shoes and coat, ready to leave, Lenore hovered by the door, tail wagging. Of course, Jon couldn't resist her. He knew she loved riding in the car too. "Come on then, girl," he said, and she followed him out to the car.

On the journey, Lenore hung her head out of the part-open window. She loved taking in all the sights and smells as they passed. Jon looked at her tail wagging happily, and smiled.

He found a spot on the edge of town, with lovely views out towards the countryside, and stopped. He left Lenore in the car with the window open a little, and then started to set up his camera and other equipment. He spotted a girl nearby and waved hello. She had also stopped to take in the view, and was eating her lunch.

Then, quick as a flash, Jon saw a blur of black fur rush by. He tried to take in what had happened. "Ah . . ." He should have known. It was Lenore, and there was food involved!

The girl had dropped some of her lunch – it was a spring roll – on the ground. Almost before she even knew it was gone, Lenore had managed to squeeze her way out of the window and wolf it down.

"Can I buy you another one?" Jon asked, heading over to try and get Lenore back into the car.

But the girl didn't even seem to notice Jon – or her missing lunch! She was hugging and cooing over Lenore instead. "Awww, puppy!" she cried, stroking her.

Lenore was so cute, she really could get away with anything!

JON AND LENORE'S DAY

5 a.m. Lenore stirs, creeps up to put her head on Jon's shoulder, and then nibbles on his chin before going back to sleep. It always makes Jon smile.

6 a.m. Jon switches on the light and reads for a little while. Rose comes in and sits at the foot of the bed, Izzy curls up under it, but Lenore lies as close to Jon as possible, tight against his back or his neck – wherever is warmest.

Jon showers, and then puts his clothes and boots on. As soon as he does this, all the dogs bound down the stairs and head for the door. They rush up the slope next to the farmhouse and do their doggy business.

When they come back inside, Jon feeds them. Lenore is especially excited by the food, of course: she wriggles and waggles, nearly falling headfirst into her breakfast because she's so happy to see it. She chomps down the food quickly – normally finishing before Rose has even started!

7 a.m. They all go to the woods for their first walk of the day. Rose and Izzy bound off immediately. Lenore follows, but she's nowhere near as fast. Every day it's a little while before she realizes that she can't keep up with them. At first she tries to follow them on her little legs, before giving up and turning back to walk with Jon.

During the walk the dogs all do their obedience exercises. *Sit. Lie. Stay.* These are very important as they ensure that the dogs remain calm and well-behaved

Back at the farmhouse, Jon puts some peanut butter on a rawhide stick and gives one to each of the dogs. Rose runs off out of sight with hers, Izzy sniffs and stares at his for a while before deciding to chew. But Lenore pounces on hers immediately, excitedly taking it over to the porch to munch straightaway!

Then it's time for Jon's breakfast: he goes inside to eat and ring Paula. He waits for Annie to arrive so they can do the farm chores together. Then he lights the wood stove and gets down to work.

Once the farm jobs are done, it's writing time. Lenore crawls under Jon's desk while he works, and doesn't move until he is done.

As the day progresses, Rose and Izzy never stop investigating things around the farm. Rose checks on the sheep, and Izzy looks out of the window to see who's driving by. But Lenore doesn't move from her spot unless Jon goes somewhere.

11.30 a.m. They go for another walk late in the morning and at lunch time – it's important for dogs to get lots of exercise and fresh air. After that, Rose and Jon will herd the sheep – or, if it's wet, the dogs will hang out by the stove while Jon writes some more.

3 p.m. Later in the afternoon they play with a ball for a while, then walk through the barn and check on the farm animals. Then it's doggy feeding time again!

8 p.m. When it gets dark, Lenore prowls through the house collecting chewbones and toys until she finds Jon and curls up at his feet or next to him on the sofa to have her belly scratched. *I love everybody,* she seems to be saying. *But you most of all.*

If Jon stays up later than she wants, Lenore goes upstairs to sleep by herself and waits for him to come and help her up onto the bed. She's like a hot-water bottle in the winter, and in the night she often crawls up to Jon's face and gives him a lick. He kisses her on the nose, and then they both go back to sleep, peaceful and happy.

CHAPTER THIRTEEN

Into the Woods

In the spring time, when the days got lighter and the weather warmer, Jon decided to take Lenore on a camping trip. Annie had agreed to look after the farm while they were away, and Jon thought it would be a great chance for him and Lenore to spend some time together, just the two of them, and practise all their training exercises without all the distractions of the farm.

Jon had been camping many times before

and he loved it, but now the time had come, he began to worry. All sorts of questions ran through his head: *Could Lenore handle the mile-long walk through the woods to the cabin they were staying in? Would she stay close and not run off? Would all her training work when they weren't at home?*

They were all packed up, but Jon was a little nervous as they began their walk towards their cabin. However, after only a few minutes, Jon realized that he needn't have worried at all. Lenore stayed close by his side, as usual . . . Until she spotted somebody else, that is!

First of all she saw a family with two children. She rushed over immediately, barking happily. *Hello!* she seemed to be saying. *I'm Lenore. Who are you?* She ran around the legs of the little boy and girl, and rubbed herself against them to make friends. They whooped excitedly and bent down to give her a hug.

Jon smiled proudly, but called her back so

that everyone could get on with their walk! But Lenore's friendliness wasn't over yet. As soon as the next people came into view – two friends out for a walk – she raced over, barking loudly. When she'd finished saying hello to them, there was a nearby elderly couple to visit.

This walk was taking such a long time because Lenore was so friendly. Jon was sure that she would have happily trotted off with each of her new friends if he hadn't called her back!

They finally made it to the cabin they were staying in, and Lenore was just as excited by that. "Here we are, girl!" Jon said as he showed her inside. She raced around, investigating every corner. She kept rushing outside and looking at the woods all around, and then coming back inside to see the cabin.

"I think we'll have a good time here, Lenore, don't you?" Jon said, grinning at his excited little dog.

That night, exhausted by the walk and exploring everywhere, Lenore lay outside the cabin under the stars. She watched intently, gnawing on a stick, as Jon read his book and took some photographs.

Just a few minutes later, he looked up from his camera to check on her – he was worried that she might run off into the woods. With her jet-black coat, there was no way he would find her amongst the shadowy trees. But again, he needn't have worried – Lenore had fallen fast asleep!

Jon scooped her up, just as he would have done at home, and put her on his bunk. When he was ready for bed too, he got into his sleeping bag. Lenore snuggled up against him like a little hot-water bottle and, worn out from her busy day, did not move all night.

Jon and Lenore spent a perfect two days and nights together. Lenore was wonderfully behaved, and she loved having Jon's attention on her the whole time, with none of the other Bedlam Farm animals to distract him! If Jon stopped to stare at a beautiful view, so did Lenore. If he sat down on a log to catch his breath, so did Lenore. And when the trip was over and they made their way back through the woods to the car, Lenore held her head high – she was very proud – and so she should be!

The camping trip only proved to Jon that Lenore was the perfect dog – well-trained, gentle and loving. She adored people, just like Izzy, and Jon wondered if she might be as good as her Bedlam Farm friend at cheering people up and visiting sick patients. He was sure that anybody who saw her cute little face would smile – and what could be better than that if you were feeling ill?

Jon decided he'd like to try her out with some patients. She was checked out by a vet, just as Izzy had been, to confirm that she was well-behaved and calm enough to be around people. Of course, she passed, just as Izzy had! She hadn't undergone all the training Izzy had yet, but she was so good with people that Jon was sure she'd be OK.

A few weeks after they came back from their camping trip, the three of them – Izzy, Lenore and Jon – set off together. They were heading for Lenore's first training session!

Keith greeted Lenore just as enthusiastically as he had Izzy. He had even made her a name badge too.

Lenore
Katz

But Lenore wasn't interested in the badge; she had spotted the huge snacks table! It was covered with doughnuts and biscuits and other yummy treats. "Oh, no!" Jon muttered, and he reached out for her. But for once, Lenore didn't make straight for the food. She suddenly spotted all these new people and was distracted by them!

The little puppy bounded to and fro across the room, and excitedly put her paws on everyone's knees in turn. *Hello!* she yapped at all the volunteers. *Hello!* Then she jumped up to kiss them all.

Jon finally caught up with her and tried to calm her down. "Off," he said gently, tugging her away from a young man and trying to get her to stay by his side. For a moment she let Jon pat her on the head, but then she remembered that there was food! She began exploring the room again, sniffing about for crumbs and scraps of food.

This went on for the whole time Keith was speaking. Jon had to follow her about to stop her pouncing on the snack table! Every time Izzy moved anywhere, so did Lenore. Jon just couldn't concentrate on the meeting at all because he was so worried about where Lenore was and what she was doing. Finally he put her on his lap and she snuggled in against his chest as usual; he looked down at her, she looked up at him – and they smiled at each other.

When the meeting ended, Jon didn't move for a moment. Lenore was snoozing now, with no idea of what was going on around her. He bent and kissed her, and she woke, reached up with her little pink tongue and kissed him back. But she didn't want to snuggle for long; she was quickly distracted by some cookies under one of the tables!

Even in the car park, Lenore sniffed around for something more to eat. She really was always hungry!

As Jon struggled to call her into the car, he thought about the gorgeous little creature who had found her way into his life. Lenore had lots and lots of good things about her; she was, in lots of ways, the perfect dog. But Jon now realized that she was not perfect for this job in the way that Izzy had been. She had changed his life and cheered him up – Jon would for ever be grateful to her – but for now, he would just let her be and not try and force her into doing something she was not suited to.

He wrapped his arms around her and said, "Thank you for being you."

Lenore thumped her tail, licked his nose and then curled up against him again. It was time to go home to the farm.

CAUTION

It's hard to meet – or read about – a Labrador like Lenore and not want one for yourself. They are beautiful, intelligent dogs. But this breed isn't for everyone. Nor are Border collies. Rose and Izzy are magnificent animals, but they might not be the right breed of dog for you.

If you are thinking of getting a dog, do talk to breeders, vets and other owners and make sure that you get the right one for you, and for your lifestyle. Labradors can be difficult – there are lots of other breeds of dog to choose from.

Good rescue centres and dog breeders will always ask you lots of questions about your home and how much time you have available before they will let you have a dog. If they don't, you should go elsewhere.

You should always get a dog from a registered breeder, or from an official rescue centre.

Never go to a pet shop as their puppies may have come from puppy farmers – breeders out to make a quick profit who may not care about the health and welfare of their dogs.

For further information on dogs and dog ownership in the UK

The Kennel Club
www.thekennelclub.org

The Kennel Club was founded in 1873 and aims to "promote in every way the general improvement of dogs". They can provide lots of information and advice on dog welfare, health, training and breeding. They can also put you in touch with registered breeders of different kinds of dog. The breeders on their register sign up to recommended breeding guidelines.

The RSPCA

If you suspect a dog is being ill-treated or the owners need some help in knowing what their dog needs – for example, a Border collie would find it almost intolerable being shut in a flat on its own all day – call the RSPCA, and they will be able to offer advice, or will call round to see the dog. They also offer lots of advice for dog owners, including on buying a puppy and finding the right breed for you.

www.rspca.org.uk

24-hour cruelty and advice line: 0300 1234 999

Border Collie Rescue

This registered charity takes in, cares for, rehabilitates, retrains and re-homes Border collies and working sheepdogs. They also provide lots of advice and information about the breed. They are based in the UK, but they have contact links to animal rescue groups in 127 different countries.

www.bordercollierescue.org

ABOUT THE AUTHOR

Jon Katz lives on Bedlam Farm in New York, USA, with his dogs, sheep, donkeys, cat, irritable rooster Winston and three hens. He has written lots of books for adults and children, and writes regular newspaper columns about dogs and about living in the country.

For further information see

www.bedlamfarm.com

Read on for a sneak peek at another of Jon Katz's wonderful real-life stories . . .

THE TOTALLY TRUE STORY OF

DEVON

The Naughtiest Dog in the World

INTRODUCTION

This is a true story.

I love my dogs, and life with dogs is – for me – very rewarding. Dogs love purely and powerfully and without complications, and I feel so lucky to be able to share my life with them.

Devon is the Border collie star of this book and I hope you will enjoy meeting him as much as I enjoyed writing about him. This book first appeared as a longer book for adult readers, but when I travelled around with the book and my dogs (they came too, of course), we met lots of young people who wanted to know about them, and parents who asked if I could write the book again for their children to read.

This book is the result.

And my dogs (*almost* all of them) have loved children. Only Devon wasn't sure at first. But if you read his story, you will understand more about Devon – and about the challenge he brought to me in a very special dog year . . .

Jon Katz

CHAPTER ONE

One Man and His Dogs

It was morning in the Katz household and Jon, who worked as a writer, was just waking up. His dark hair rested on the pillow, and his glasses on the bedside table twinkled in the early morning sunlight.

Downstairs, Julius and Stanley, the family's two dogs, snoozed happily too. Their ears twitched, their paws shifted position now and then – and sometimes they let out a rumble of doggy snores.

Julius and Stanley were Labradors – big dogs

with silky golden coats the colour of butter, floppy ears and long wagging tails. They had lived with Jon and his wife, Paula, for a long time now and they all loved each other more than anything.

Jon had brought Julius home when he was just a puppy. "I've got a surprise for you!" he'd told Emma, his daughter, holding the wriggling doggy bundle out to the little girl, smiling at the puzzled frown on her face.

Emma had looked amazed as she'd moved her head close to Julius's.

Looking up at the shrieking girl, Julius had blinked, stuck out his long tongue and licked her nose. Jon had patted the puppy's head, and Julius had licked him too. They looked at each other for a moment, and somehow both of them had known at once that they would be friends.

A year later, his cousin Stanley had arrived. He came from the same breeder as Julius, and looked almost identical to the older dog when *he*'d moved in.

This tiny new puppy had melted Jon's heart straight away, though he had wondered whether

Julius would take to the newcomer. However, Stanley had soon won him over, and within a couple of days the two dogs loved each other and their new family as much as Jon and his family loved them.

It was now seven years since Stanley had joined the family. He and Julius were much bigger – and still the best of friends. Julius was eight years old and Stanley seven, but sometimes they behaved as if they were much older! They were both lazy dogs: all they wanted to do most of the time was rest! Sometimes Stanley would summon up the energy to chase a ball or have a swim in a pond, but apart from that the Labradors' days proceeded at a nice, comfortable, relaxed pace and they were happy with their quiet life!

Jon came downstairs for a glass of water and looked in on the dogs, waking them. As he went back upstairs, they followed him for their morning cuddle. Jon smiled, as he did every time he looked at his calm and loving pets, thinking for the millionth time how lucky he was to have them.

Dog Report	
Name:	*Julius*
Age:	*Eight*
Breed:	*Golden Labrador*
Lives:	*With Jon and Paula, in New York*
Friends:	*Everybody! But especially Jon and Stanley*
Likes:	*Sleeping, lots of hugs, rawhide chews, dinner, walks, sniffing interesting smells, staring at the tops of mountains for hours*
Doesn't like:	*Rainy days (he's allergic to rainy days), the sea (he's allergic to sea water)*

Dog Report	
Name:	Stanley
Age:	Seven
Breed:	Golden Labrador
Lives:	With Jon and Paula, in New York
Friends:	Everybody! But especially Jon and Julius
Likes:	Sleeping, lots of hugs, biscuits, dinner, chasing balls, sniffing interesting smells, swimming in ponds, playing tug-of-war with rope toys
Doesn't like:	Rainy days

A typical day for Jon, Julius and Stanley:

Getting up

Neither dog moves a muscle until Jon is awake, then they slither into his bed for a big furry family cuddle. Wet noses and the odd lick are normal! After Jon is up, they sit quietly and attentively under the kitchen table, staring at their food bowls. *If we stare hard enough and long enough, will our food magically appear?* they wonder!

Early walk

This is a leisurely stroll of about half an hour through the local neighbourhood. Julius and Stanley want to sniff *everything*. No shrub or rock is missed and nothing can distract them when they smell something particularly interesting. The walks are peaceful, and they meet lots of dog buddies, friends and admirers. Everyone likes Julius and Stanley and the local children wave at them from bikes and car windows.

Note: Labradors are supposed to be hunting dogs – outdoor working dogs – but Julius and Stanley have never been keen on rain or snow. If the weather is nasty, they have mastered a hundred-metre dash to the nearest tree, and then they want to go back inside. This suits Jon nicely – he's not keen on walking in the rain either!

Snack time

This is two big rawhide chews with a layer of peanut butter in between. Jules and Stanley carry these treats into the garden and settle down for a good gnaw. This kind of thing can be pretty tiring for a dog and they need a good long rest afterwards, sometimes rousing themselves from their nap to bark at a passing dog. Mostly not.

Daytime

Jon works from home as a writer, which means he gets to spend *lots* of time with Stanley and Julius. It's a good thing they all get along so well! He works in his study; if it's rainy, the two dogs come in and act as footrests, both tucked underneath his desk, one on the left, one on the right; otherwise they nap in the sun. The dogs are clever, knowing exactly when Jon has an important deadline and needs to be left in peace.

Afternoon walk

This is maybe a mile or so, but no one's in any hurry – it's a gentle stroll.

More snacks

Jon knows that he shouldn't give his boys snacks, but he can't resist offering them rawhide chews, pigs' ears and dog biscuits . . .

Dinner

Julius and Stanley like this time of day! But it doesn't take them long to scoff down their food.

Bedtime

As night falls, so the Labs settle down on their

beds for a final snack and then fall into a deep, unmoving sleep.

Later, out on their morning walk, Julius and Stanley padded along the familiar pavements, totally contented. After a while Stanley nipped Jon's bottom to get his attention. He wanted Jon to throw his ball for him to go and catch.

He didn't need to do anything else: Jon knew exactly what he wanted and threw the ball into the grass ahead. Stanley yapped happily and raced after it.

We could all do this in our sleep, Jon thought as they strolled along. They were almost like a school of fish, the three of them, veering first in one direction, then another. They turned corners at the same time, knew each other's moods and were happy sitting in silence together in various parks and gardens, sharing their lunch.

The three of them enjoyed their walk in the sun, little knowing that things were about to change for ever. And the change was coming on four legs . . .

Meet some more of the Bedlam Farm animals . .

Jon Katz

Jon has always enjoyed a peaceful life. But when he agrees to give a home to Devon, an abandoned little Border collie, things will never be the same again!

From the moment mischievous Devon explodes out of his cage at the airport, Jon realizes there's going to be trouble. And over the course of the next year, he finds out just how much trouble one little dog can be!

Chasing buses, herding sheep and stealing

ISBN: 9781849412780

THE TOTALLY TRUE STORY OF

ROSE & IZZY

The Cheekiest Dogs on the Farm

Jon Katz

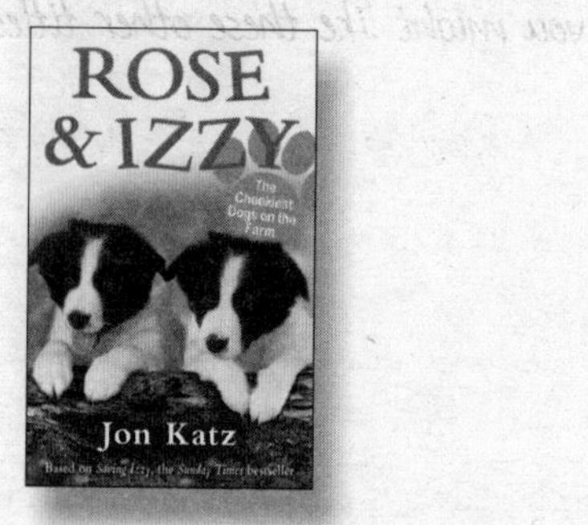

Meet Izzy when he first joins Bedlam Farm . . .

Looking after the dogs, sheep, donkeys, hens, rooster and cat on Bedlam Farm is hard work! But Jon is lucky enough to have Rose, the brave Border collie, always at his side.

When Jon hears about Izzy, an abandoned dog kept alone in a field, he can't bear to leave him, and agrees to take him in. Life is just about to get even busier! But Jon soon realizes that cheeky little Izzy is a problem that even Rose can't help him with!

ISBN: 9781849412780

If you enjoy reading about the animals of Bedlam Farm, you might like these other titles published by Random House Children's Books . . .

Norton

The loveable cat who travelled the world

PETER GETHERS

Peter Gethers hates cats. That is until he meets Norton, a very cute, very friendly Scottish Fold kitten.

Soon Peter and Norton are inseparable, travelling together on trains and boats, in planes and cars all over the world! Eating at restaurants, making new friends and meeting famous movie stars – read all about these and Norton's other real-life adventures in this wonderful true story.

ISBN: 978 1 849 41387 9

CHRISTIAN THE LION

Anthony Bourke and John Rendall

The true story of one lion's search for a home . . .

For sale: lion cubs, in Harrods department store!

Imagine the surprise on shoppers' faces when they see a pair of beautiful little lion cubs for sale in London! Two friends, Ace and John, can't bear to leave the male cub behind, stuck in such a tiny cage.

So they take him home with them, and they name him Christian. But it's not long before the cheeky lion is getting into all sorts of mischief and sticky situations!

Whatever will they do when Christian changes from a cute and cuddly little cub into a powerful and noble beast . . . ?

ISBN: 978 1 862 30956 2

Look out for the Battersea Dogs & Cats Home series!